keepsakes

memories

Love wholeheartedly, be surprised, give thanks and praise- Then you will discover the fullness of your life.
-Brother David Steindl-Rast

Day/Date   Be sure to remember five things to be grateful for every day.

Day/Date   Be sure to remember five things to be grateful for every day.

Day/Date   Be sure to remember five things to be grateful for every day.

Love wholeheartedly, be surprised, give thanks and praise- Then you will discover the fullness of your life.
-Brother David Steindl-Rast

Day/Date   Be sure to remember five things to be grateful for every day.

Day/Date   Be sure to remember five things to be grateful for every day.

Day/Date   Be sure to remember five things to be grateful for every day.

Love wholeheartedly, be surprised, give thanks and praise- Then you will discover the fullness of your life.
-Brother David Steindl-Rast

Day/Date   Be sure to remember five things to be grateful for every day.

Day/Date   Be sure to remember five things to be grateful for every day.

Day/Date   Be sure to remember five things to be grateful for every day.

Love wholeheartedly, be surprised, give thanks and praise- Then you will discover the fullness of your life.
-Brother David Steindl-Rast

Day/Date   Be sure to remember five things to be grateful for every day.

Day/Date   Be sure to remember five things to be grateful for every day.

Day/Date   Be sure to remember five things to be grateful for every day.

Love wholeheartedly, be surprised, give thanks and praise- Then you will discover the fullness of your life.
-Brother David Steindl-Rast

Day/Date   Be sure to remember five things to be grateful for every day.

Day/Date   Be sure to remember five things to be grateful for every day.

Day/Date   Be sure to remember five things to be grateful for every day.

Love wholeheartedly, be surprised, give thanks and praise- Then you will discover the fullness of your life.
-Brother David Steindl-Rast

Day/Date   Be sure to remember five things to be grateful for every day.

Day/Date   Be sure to remember five things to be grateful for every day.

Day/Date   Be sure to remember five things to be grateful for every day.

Love wholeheartedly, be surprised, give thanks and praise- Then you will discover the fullness of your life.
-Brother David Steindl-Rast

Day/Date   Be sure to remember five things to be grateful for every day.

Day/Date   Be sure to remember five things to be grateful for every day.

Day/Date   Be sure to remember five things to be grateful for every day.

Love wholeheartedly, be surprised, give thanks and praise- Then you will discover the fullness of your life.
-Brother David Steindl-Rast

Day/Date   Be sure to remember five things to be grateful for every day.

Day/Date   Be sure to remember five things to be grateful for every day.

Day/Date   Be sure to remember five things to be grateful for every day.

Love wholeheartedly, be surprised, give thanks and praise- Then you will discover the fullness of your life.
-Brother David Steindl-Rast

Day/Date   Be sure to remember five things to be grateful for every day.

Day/Date   Be sure to remember five things to be grateful for every day.

Day/Date   Be sure to remember five things to be grateful for every day.

Love wholeheartedly, be surprised, give thanks and praise- Then you will discover the fullness of your life.
-Brother David Steindl-Rast

Day/Date   Be sure to remember five things to be grateful for every day.

Day/Date   Be sure to remember five things to be grateful for every day.

Day/Date   Be sure to remember five things to be grateful for every day.

Love wholeheartedly, be surprised, give thanks and praise- Then you will discover the fullness of your life.
-Brother David Steindl-Rast

Day/Date   Be sure to remember five things to be grateful for every day.

Day/Date   Be sure to remember five things to be grateful for every day.

Day/Date   Be sure to remember five things to be grateful for every day.

Love wholeheartedly, be surprised, give thanks and praise- Then you will discover the fullness of your life.
-Brother David Steindl-Rast

Day/Date   Be sure to remember five things to be grateful for every day.

Day/Date   Be sure to remember five things to be grateful for every day.

Day/Date   Be sure to remember five things to be grateful for every day.

Love wholeheartedly, be surprised, give thanks and praise- Then you will discover the fullness of your life.
-Brother David Steindl-Rast

Day/Date   Be sure to remember five things to be grateful for every day.

Day/Date   Be sure to remember five things to be grateful for every day.

Day/Date   Be sure to remember five things to be grateful for every day.

Love wholeheartedly, be surprised, give thanks and praise- Then you will discover the fullness of your life.
-Brother David Steindl-Rast

Day/Date   Be sure to remember five things to be grateful for every day.

Day/Date   Be sure to remember five things to be grateful for every day.

Day/Date   Be sure to remember five things to be grateful for every day.

Love wholeheartedly, be surprised, give thanks and praise- Then you will discover the fullness of your life.
-Brother David Steindl-Rast

Day/Date   Be sure to remember five things to be grateful for every day.

Day/Date   Be sure to remember five things to be grateful for every day.

Day/Date   Be sure to remember five things to be grateful for every day.

Love wholeheartedly, be surprised, give thanks and praise- Then you will discover the fullness of your life.
-Brother David Steindl-Rast

Day/Date   Be sure to remember five things to be grateful for every day.

Day/Date   Be sure to remember five things to be grateful for every day.

Day/Date   Be sure to remember five things to be grateful for every day.

Love wholeheartedly, be surprised, give thanks and praise- Then you will discover the fullness of your life.
-Brother David Steindl-Rast

Day/Date   Be sure to remember five things to be grateful for every day.

Day/Date   Be sure to remember five things to be grateful for every day.

Day/Date   Be sure to remember five things to be grateful for every day.

Love wholeheartedly, be surprised, give thanks and praise- Then you will discover the fullness of your life.
-Brother David Steindl-Rast

Day/Date   Be sure to remember five things to be grateful for every day.

Day/Date   Be sure to remember five things to be grateful for every day.

Day/Date   Be sure to remember five things to be grateful for every day.

Love wholeheartedly, be surprised, give thanks and praise- Then you will discover the fullness of your life.
-Brother David Steindl-Rast

Day/Date   Be sure to remember five things to be grateful for every day.

Day/Date   Be sure to remember five things to be grateful for every day.

Day/Date   Be sure to remember five things to be grateful for every day.

Love wholeheartedly, be surprised, give thanks and praise- Then you will discover the fullness of your life.
-Brother David Steindl-Rast

Day/Date   Be sure to remember five things to be grateful for every day.

Day/Date   Be sure to remember five things to be grateful for every day.

Day/Date   Be sure to remember five things to be grateful for every day.

Love wholeheartedly, be surprised, give thanks and praise- Then you will discover the fullness of your life.
-Brother David Steindl-Rast

Day/Date   Be sure to remember five things to be grateful for every day.

Day/Date   Be sure to remember five things to be grateful for every day.

Day/Date   Be sure to remember five things to be grateful for every day.

Love wholeheartedly, be surprised, give thanks and praise- Then you will discover the fullness of your life.
-Brother David Steindl-Rast

Day/Date   Be sure to remember five things to be grateful for every day.

Day/Date   Be sure to remember five things to be grateful for every day.

Day/Date   Be sure to remember five things to be grateful for every day.

Love wholeheartedly, be surprised, give thanks and praise- Then you will discover the fullness of your life.
-Brother David Steindl-Rast

Day/Date   Be sure to remember five things to be grateful for every day.

Day/Date   Be sure to remember five things to be grateful for every day.

Day/Date   Be sure to remember five things to be grateful for every day.

Love wholeheartedly, be surprised, give thanks and praise- Then you will discover the fullness of your life.
-Brother David Steindl-Rast

Day/Date   Be sure to remember five things to be grateful for every day.

Day/Date   Be sure to remember five things to be grateful for every day.

Day/Date   Be sure to remember five things to be grateful for every day.

Love wholeheartedly, be surprised, give thanks and praise- Then you will discover the fullness of your life.
-Brother David Steindl-Rast

Day/Date   Be sure to remember five things to be grateful for every day.

Day/Date   Be sure to remember five things to be grateful for every day.

Day/Date   Be sure to remember five things to be grateful for every day.

Love wholeheartedly, be surprised, give thanks and praise- Then you will discover the fullness of your life.
-Brother David Steindl-Rast

Day/Date   Be sure to remember five things to be grateful for every day.

Day/Date   Be sure to remember five things to be grateful for every day.

Day/Date   Be sure to remember five things to be grateful for every day.

Love wholeheartedly, be surprised, give thanks and praise- Then you will discover the fullness of your life.
-Brother David Steindl-Rast

Day/Date   Be sure to remember five things to be grateful for every day.

Day/Date   Be sure to remember five things to be grateful for every day.

Day/Date   Be sure to remember five things to be grateful for every day.

Love wholeheartedly, be surprised, give thanks and praise- Then you will discover the fullness of your life.
-Brother David Steindl-Rast

Day/Date   Be sure to remember five things to be grateful for every day.

Day/Date   Be sure to remember five things to be grateful for every day.

Day/Date   Be sure to remember five things to be grateful for every day.

Love wholeheartedly, be surprised, give thanks and praise- Then you will discover the fullness of your life.
-Brother David Steindl-Rast

Day/Date   Be sure to remember five things to be grateful for every day.

Day/Date   Be sure to remember five things to be grateful for every day.

Day/Date   Be sure to remember five things to be grateful for every day.

Love wholeheartedly, be surprised, give thanks and praise- Then you will discover the fullness of your life.
-Brother David Steindl-Rast

Day/Date   Be sure to remember five things to be grateful for every day.

Day/Date   Be sure to remember five things to be grateful for every day.

Day/Date   Be sure to remember five things to be grateful for every day.

Love wholeheartedly, be surprised, give thanks and praise- Then you will discover the fullness of your life.
-Brother David Steindl-Rast

Day/Date   Be sure to remember five things to be grateful for every day.

Day/Date   Be sure to remember five things to be grateful for every day.

Day/Date   Be sure to remember five things to be grateful for every day.

Love wholeheartedly, be surprised, give thanks and praise- Then you will discover the fullness of your life.
-Brother David Steindl-Rast

Day/Date   Be sure to remember five things to be grateful for every day.

Day/Date   Be sure to remember five things to be grateful for every day.

Day/Date   Be sure to remember five things to be grateful for every day.

Love wholeheartedly, be surprised, give thanks and praise- Then you will discover the fullness of your life.
-Brother David Steindl-Rast

Day/Date   Be sure to remember five things to be grateful for every day.

Day/Date   Be sure to remember five things to be grateful for every day.

Day/Date   Be sure to remember five things to be grateful for every day.

Love wholeheartedly, be surprised, give thanks and praise- Then you will discover the fullness of your life.
-Brother David Steindl-Rast

Day/Date   Be sure to remember five things to be grateful for every day.

Day/Date   Be sure to remember five things to be grateful for every day.

Day/Date   Be sure to remember five things to be grateful for every day.

Love wholeheartedly, be surprised, give thanks and praise- Then you will discover the fullness of your life.
-Brother David Steindl-Rast

Day/Date   Be sure to remember five things to be grateful for every day.

Day/Date   Be sure to remember five things to be grateful for every day.

Day/Date   Be sure to remember five things to be grateful for every day.

Love wholeheartedly, be surprised, give thanks and praise- Then you will discover the fullness of your life.
-Brother David Steindl-Rast

Day/Date   Be sure to remember five things to be grateful for every day.

Day/Date   Be sure to remember five things to be grateful for every day.

Day/Date   Be sure to remember five things to be grateful for every day.

Love wholeheartedly, be surprised, give thanks and praise- Then you will discover the fullness of your life.
-Brother David Steindl-Rast

Day/Date   Be sure to remember five things to be grateful for every day.

Day/Date   Be sure to remember five things to be grateful for every day.

Day/Date   Be sure to remember five things to be grateful for every day.

Love wholeheartedly, be surprised, give thanks and praise- Then you will discover the fullness of your life.
-Brother David Steindl-Rast

Day/Date   Be sure to remember five things to be grateful for every day.

Day/Date   Be sure to remember five things to be grateful for every day.

Day/Date   Be sure to remember five things to be grateful for every day.

Love wholeheartedly, be surprised, give thanks and praise- Then you will discover the fullness of your life.
-Brother David Steindl-Rast

Day/Date   Be sure to remember five things to be grateful for every day.

Day/Date   Be sure to remember five things to be grateful for every day.

Day/Date   Be sure to remember five things to be grateful for every day.

Love wholeheartedly, be surprised, give thanks and praise- Then you will discover the fullness of your life.
-Brother David Steindl-Rast

Day/Date   Be sure to remember five things to be grateful for every day.

Day/Date   Be sure to remember five things to be grateful for every day.

Day/Date   Be sure to remember five things to be grateful for every day.

Love wholeheartedly, be surprised, give thanks and praise- Then you will discover the fullness of your life.
-Brother David Steindl-Rast

Day/Date   Be sure to remember five things to be grateful for every day.

Day/Date   Be sure to remember five things to be grateful for every day.

Day/Date   Be sure to remember five things to be grateful for every day.

Love wholeheartedly, be surprised, give thanks and praise- Then you will discover the fullness of your life.
-Brother David Steindl-Rast

Day/Date   Be sure to remember five things to be grateful for every day.

Day/Date   Be sure to remember five things to be grateful for every day.

Day/Date   Be sure to remember five things to be grateful for every day.

Love wholeheartedly, be surprised, give thanks and praise- Then you will discover the fullness of your life.
-Brother David Steindl-Rast

Day/Date   Be sure to remember five things to be grateful for every day.

Day/Date   Be sure to remember five things to be grateful for every day.

Day/Date   Be sure to remember five things to be grateful for every day.

Love wholeheartedly, be surprised, give thanks and praise- Then you will discover the fullness of your life.
-Brother David Steindl-Rast

Day/Date   Be sure to remember five things to be grateful for every day.

Day/Date   Be sure to remember five things to be grateful for every day.

Day/Date   Be sure to remember five things to be grateful for every day.

Love wholeheartedly, be surprised, give thanks and praise- Then you will discover the fullness of your life.
-Brother David Steindl-Rast

Day/Date   Be sure to remember five things to be grateful for every day.

Day/Date   Be sure to remember five things to be grateful for every day.

Day/Date   Be sure to remember five things to be grateful for every day.

Love wholeheartedly, be surprised, give thanks and praise- Then you will discover the fullness of your life.
-Brother David Steindl-Rast

Day/Date   Be sure to remember five things to be grateful for every day.

Day/Date   Be sure to remember five things to be grateful for every day.

Day/Date   Be sure to remember five things to be grateful for every day.

Love wholeheartedly, be surprised, give thanks and praise- Then you will discover the fullness of your life.
-Brother David Steindl-Rast

Day/Date   Be sure to remember five things to be grateful for every day.

Day/Date   Be sure to remember five things to be grateful for every day.

Day/Date   Be sure to remember five things to be grateful for every day.

Love wholeheartedly, be surprised, give thanks and praise- Then you will discover the fullness of your life.
-Brother David Steindl-Rast

Day/Date   Be sure to remember five things to be grateful for every day.

Day/Date   Be sure to remember five things to be grateful for every day.

Day/Date   Be sure to remember five things to be grateful for every day.

Love wholeheartedly, be surprised, give thanks and praise- Then you will discover the fullness of your life.
-Brother David Steindl-Rast

Day/Date   Be sure to remember five things to be grateful for every day.

Day/Date   Be sure to remember five things to be grateful for every day.

Day/Date   Be sure to remember five things to be grateful for every day.

Love wholeheartedly, be surprised, give thanks and praise- Then you will discover the fullness of your life.
-Brother David Steindl-Rast

Day/Date   Be sure to remember five things to be grateful for every day.

Day/Date   Be sure to remember five things to be grateful for every day.

Day/Date   Be sure to remember five things to be grateful for every day.

Love wholeheartedly, be surprised, give thanks and praise- Then you will discover the fullness of your life.
-Brother David Steindl-Rast

Day/Date   Be sure to remember five things to be grateful for every day.

Day/Date   Be sure to remember five things to be grateful for every day.

Day/Date   Be sure to remember five things to be grateful for every day.

Love wholeheartedly, be surprised, give thanks and praise- Then you will discover the fullness of your life.
-Brother David Steindl-Rast

Day/Date   Be sure to remember five things to be grateful for every day.

Day/Date   Be sure to remember five things to be grateful for every day.

Day/Date   Be sure to remember five things to be grateful for every day.

Love wholeheartedly, be surprised, give thanks and praise- Then you will discover the fullness of your life.
-Brother David Steindl-Rast

Day/Date   Be sure to remember five things to be grateful for every day.

Day/Date   Be sure to remember five things to be grateful for every day.

Day/Date   Be sure to remember five things to be grateful for every day.

Love wholeheartedly, be surprised, give thanks and praise- Then you will discover the fullness of your life.
-Brother David Steindl-Rast

Day/Date   Be sure to remember five things to be grateful for every day.

Day/Date   Be sure to remember five things to be grateful for every day.

Day/Date   Be sure to remember five things to be grateful for every day.

Love wholeheartedly, be surprised, give thanks and praise- Then you will discover the fullness of your life.
-Brother David Steindl-Rast

Day/Date   Be sure to remember five things to be grateful for every day.

Day/Date   Be sure to remember five things to be grateful for every day.

Day/Date   Be sure to remember five things to be grateful for every day.

Love wholeheartedly, be surprised, give thanks and praise- Then you will discover the fullness of your life.
-Brother David Steindl-Rast

Day/Date   Be sure to remember five things to be grateful for every day.

Day/Date   Be sure to remember five things to be grateful for every day.

Day/Date   Be sure to remember five things to be grateful for every day.

Love wholeheartedly, be surprised, give thanks and praise- Then you will discover the fullness of your life.
-Brother David Steindl-Rast

Day/Date   Be sure to remember five things to be grateful for every day.

Day/Date   Be sure to remember five things to be grateful for every day.

Day/Date   Be sure to remember five things to be grateful for every day.

Love wholeheartedly, be surprised, give thanks and praise- Then you will discover the fullness of your life.
-Brother David Steindl-Rast

Day/Date   Be sure to remember five things to be grateful for every day.

Day/Date   Be sure to remember five things to be grateful for every day.

Day/Date   Be sure to remember five things to be grateful for every day.

Love wholeheartedly, be surprised, give thanks and praise- Then you will discover the fullness of your life.
-Brother David Steindl-Rast

Day/Date   Be sure to remember five things to be grateful for every day.

Day/Date   Be sure to remember five things to be grateful for every day.

Day/Date   Be sure to remember five things to be grateful for every day.

Love wholeheartedly, be surprised, give thanks and praise- Then you will discover the fullness of your life.
-Brother David Steindl-Rast

Day/Date   Be sure to remember five things to be grateful for every day.

Day/Date   Be sure to remember five things to be grateful for every day.

Day/Date   Be sure to remember five things to be grateful for every day.

Love wholeheartedly, be surprised, give thanks and praise- Then you will discover the fullness of your life.
-Brother David Steindl-Rast

Day/Date   Be sure to remember five things to be grateful for every day.

Day/Date   Be sure to remember five things to be grateful for every day.

Day/Date   Be sure to remember five things to be grateful for every day.

Love wholeheartedly, be surprised, give thanks and praise- Then you will discover the fullness of your life.
-Brother David Steindl-Rast

Day/Date   Be sure to remember five things to be grateful for every day.

Day/Date   Be sure to remember five things to be grateful for every day.

Day/Date   Be sure to remember five things to be grateful for every day.

Love wholeheartedly, be surprised, give thanks and praise- Then you will discover the fullness of your life.
-Brother David Steindl-Rast

Day/Date   Be sure to remember five things to be grateful for every day.

Day/Date   Be sure to remember five things to be grateful for every day.

Day/Date   Be sure to remember five things to be grateful for every day.

Love wholeheartedly, be surprised, give thanks and praise- Then you will discover the fullness of your life.
-Brother David Steindl-Rast

Day/Date   Be sure to remember five things to be grateful for every day.

Day/Date   Be sure to remember five things to be grateful for every day.

Day/Date   Be sure to remember five things to be grateful for every day.

Love wholeheartedly, be surprised, give thanks and praise- Then you will discover the fullness of your life.
-Brother David Steindl-Rast

Day/Date   Be sure to remember five things to be grateful for every day.

Day/Date   Be sure to remember five things to be grateful for every day.

Day/Date   Be sure to remember five things to be grateful for every day.

Love wholeheartedly, be surprised, give thanks and praise- Then you will discover the fullness of your life.
-Brother David Steindl-Rast

Day/Date   Be sure to remember five things to be grateful for every day.

Day/Date   Be sure to remember five things to be grateful for every day.

Day/Date   Be sure to remember five things to be grateful for every day.

Love wholeheartedly, be surprised, give thanks and praise- Then you will discover the fullness of your life.
-Brother David Steindl-Rast

Day/Date   Be sure to remember five things to be grateful for every day.

Day/Date   Be sure to remember five things to be grateful for every day.

Day/Date   Be sure to remember five things to be grateful for every day.

Love wholeheartedly, be surprised, give thanks and praise- Then you will discover the fullness of your life.
-Brother David Steindl-Rast

Day/Date   Be sure to remember five things to be grateful for every day.

Day/Date   Be sure to remember five things to be grateful for every day.

Day/Date   Be sure to remember five things to be grateful for every day.

Love wholeheartedly, be surprised, give thanks and praise- Then you will discover the fullness of your life.
-Brother David Steindl-Rast

Day/Date   Be sure to remember five things to be grateful for every day.

Day/Date   Be sure to remember five things to be grateful for every day.

Day/Date   Be sure to remember five things to be grateful for every day.

Love wholeheartedly, be surprised, give thanks and praise- Then you will discover the fullness of your life.
-Brother David Steindl-Rast

Day/Date   Be sure to remember five things to be grateful for every day.

Day/Date   Be sure to remember five things to be grateful for every day.

Day/Date   Be sure to remember five things to be grateful for every day.

Love wholeheartedly, be surprised, give thanks and praise- Then you will discover the fullness of your life.
-Brother David Steindl-Rast

Day/Date   Be sure to remember five things to be grateful for every day.

Day/Date   Be sure to remember five things to be grateful for every day.

Day/Date   Be sure to remember five things to be grateful for every day.

Love wholeheartedly, be surprised, give thanks and praise- Then you will discover the fullness of your life.
-Brother David Steindl-Rast

Day/Date   Be sure to remember five things to be grateful for every day.

Day/Date   Be sure to remember five things to be grateful for every day.

Day/Date   Be sure to remember five things to be grateful for every day.

Love wholeheartedly, be surprised, give thanks and praise- Then you will discover the fullness of your life.
-Brother David Steindl-Rast

Day/Date
Be sure to remember five things to be grateful for every day.

Day/Date
Be sure to remember five things to be grateful for every day.

Day/Date
Be sure to remember five things to be grateful for every day.

Love wholeheartedly, be surprised, give thanks and praise- Then you will discover the fullness of your life.
-Brother David Steindl-Rast

Day/Date   Be sure to remember five things to be grateful for every day.

Day/Date   Be sure to remember five things to be grateful for every day.

Day/Date   Be sure to remember five things to be grateful for every day.

Love wholeheartedly, be surprised, give thanks and praise- Then you will discover the fullness of your life.
-Brother David Steindl-Rast

Day/Date   Be sure to remember five things to be grateful for every day.

Day/Date   Be sure to remember five things to be grateful for every day.

Day/Date   Be sure to remember five things to be grateful for every day.

Love wholeheartedly, be surprised, give thanks and praise- Then you will discover the fullness of your life.
-Brother David Steindl-Rast

Day/Date   Be sure to remember five things to be grateful for every day.

Day/Date   Be sure to remember five things to be grateful for every day.

Day/Date   Be sure to remember five things to be grateful for every day.

Love wholeheartedly, be surprised, give thanks and praise- Then you will discover the fullness of your life.
-Brother David Steindl-Rast

Day/Date Be sure to remember five things to be grateful for every day.

Day/Date Be sure to remember five things to be grateful for every day.

Day/Date Be sure to remember five things to be grateful for every day.

Love wholeheartedly, be surprised, give thanks and praise- Then you will discover the fullness of your life.
-Brother David Steindl-Rast

Day/Date   Be sure to remember five things to be grateful for every day.

Day/Date   Be sure to remember five things to be grateful for every day.

Day/Date   Be sure to remember five things to be grateful for every day.

Love wholeheartedly, be surprised, give thanks and praise- Then you will discover the fullness of your life.
-Brother David Steindl-Rast

Day/Date   Be sure to remember five things to be grateful for every day.

Day/Date   Be sure to remember five things to be grateful for every day.

Day/Date   Be sure to remember five things to be grateful for every day.

Love wholeheartedly, be surprised, give thanks and praise- Then you will discover the fullness of your life.
-Brother David Steindl-Rast

Day/Date   Be sure to remember five things to be grateful for every day.

Day/Date   Be sure to remember five things to be grateful for every day.

Day/Date   Be sure to remember five things to be grateful for every day.

Love wholeheartedly, be surprised, give thanks and praise- Then you will discover the fullness of your life.
-Brother David Steindl-Rast

Day/Date   Be sure to remember five things to be grateful for every day.

Day/Date   Be sure to remember five things to be grateful for every day.

Day/Date   Be sure to remember five things to be grateful for every day.

Love wholeheartedly, be surprised, give thanks and praise- Then you will discover the fullness of your life.
-Brother David Steindl-Rast

Day/Date   Be sure to remember five things to be grateful for every day.

Day/Date   Be sure to remember five things to be grateful for every day.

Day/Date   Be sure to remember five things to be grateful for every day.

Love wholeheartedly, be surprised, give thanks and praise- Then you will discover the fullness of your life.
-Brother David Steindl-Rast

Day/Date   Be sure to remember five things to be grateful for every day.

Day/Date   Be sure to remember five things to be grateful for every day.

Day/Date   Be sure to remember five things to be grateful for every day.

Love wholeheartedly, be surprised, give thanks and praise- Then you will discover the fullness of your life.
-Brother David Steindl-Rast

Day/Date
Be sure to remember five things to be grateful for every day.

Day/Date
Be sure to remember five things to be grateful for every day.

Day/Date
Be sure to remember five things to be grateful for every day.

Love wholeheartedly, be surprised, give thanks and praise- Then you will discover the fullness of your life.
-Brother David Steindl-Rast

Day/Date   Be sure to remember five things to be grateful for every day.

Day/Date   Be sure to remember five things to be grateful for every day.

Day/Date   Be sure to remember five things to be grateful for every day.

Love wholeheartedly, be surprised, give thanks and praise- Then you will discover the fullness of your life.
-Brother David Steindl-Rast

Day/Date   Be sure to remember five things to be grateful for every day.

Day/Date   Be sure to remember five things to be grateful for every day.

Day/Date   Be sure to remember five things to be grateful for every day.

Love wholeheartedly, be surprised, give thanks and praise- Then you will discover the fullness of your life.
-Brother David Steindl-Rast

Day/Date   Be sure to remember five things to be grateful for every day.

Day/Date   Be sure to remember five things to be grateful for every day.

Day/Date   Be sure to remember five things to be grateful for every day.

Love wholeheartedly, be surprised, give thanks and praise- Then you will discover the fullness of your life.
-Brother David Steindl-Rast

Day/Date   Be sure to remember five things to be grateful for every day.

Day/Date   Be sure to remember five things to be grateful for every day.

Day/Date   Be sure to remember five things to be grateful for every day.

Love wholeheartedly, be surprised, give thanks and praise- Then you will discover the fullness of your life.
-Brother David Steindl-Rast

Day/Date   Be sure to remember five things to be grateful for every day.

Day/Date   Be sure to remember five things to be grateful for every day.

Day/Date   Be sure to remember five things to be grateful for every day.

Love wholeheartedly, be surprised, give thanks and praise- Then you will discover the fullness of your life.
-Brother David Steindl-Rast

Day/Date   Be sure to remember five things to be grateful for every day.

Day/Date   Be sure to remember five things to be grateful for every day.

Day/Date   Be sure to remember five things to be grateful for every day.

Love wholeheartedly, be surprised, give thanks and praise- Then you will discover the fullness of your life.
-Brother David Steindl-Rast

Day/Date   Be sure to remember five things to be grateful for every day.

Day/Date   Be sure to remember five things to be grateful for every day.

Day/Date   Be sure to remember five things to be grateful for every day.

Love wholeheartedly, be surprised, give thanks and praise- Then you will discover the fullness of your life.
-Brother David Steindl-Rast

Day/Date   Be sure to remember five things to be grateful for every day.

Day/Date   Be sure to remember five things to be grateful for every day.

Day/Date   Be sure to remember five things to be grateful for every day.

Love wholeheartedly, be surprised, give thanks and praise- Then you will discover the fullness of your life.
-Brother David Steindl-Rast

Day/Date   Be sure to remember five things to be grateful for every day.

Day/Date   Be sure to remember five things to be grateful for every day.

Day/Date   Be sure to remember five things to be grateful for every day.

Love wholeheartedly, be surprised, give thanks and praise- Then you will discover the fullness of your life.
-Brother David Steindl-Rast

Day/Date   Be sure to remember five things to be grateful for every day.

Day/Date   Be sure to remember five things to be grateful for every day.

Day/Date   Be sure to remember five things to be grateful for every day.

Love wholeheartedly, be surprised, give thanks and praise- Then you will discover the fullness of your life.
-Brother David Steindl-Rast

Day/Date   Be sure to remember five things to be grateful for every day.

Day/Date   Be sure to remember five things to be grateful for every day.

Day/Date   Be sure to remember five things to be grateful for every day.

Love wholeheartedly, be surprised, give thanks and praise- Then you will discover the fullness of your life.
-Brother David Steindl-Rast

Day/Date   Be sure to remember five things to be grateful for every day.

Day/Date   Be sure to remember five things to be grateful for every day.

Day/Date   Be sure to remember five things to be grateful for every day.

Love wholeheartedly, be surprised, give thanks and praise- Then you will discover the fullness of your life.
-Brother David Steindl-Rast

Day/Date   Be sure to remember five things to be grateful for every day.

Day/Date   Be sure to remember five things to be grateful for every day.

Day/Date   Be sure to remember five things to be grateful for every day.

Love wholeheartedly, be surprised, give thanks and praise- Then you will discover the fullness of your life.
-Brother David Steindl-Rast

Day/Date   Be sure to remember five things to be grateful for every day.

Day/Date   Be sure to remember five things to be grateful for every day.

Day/Date   Be sure to remember five things to be grateful for every day.

Love wholeheartedly, be surprised, give thanks and praise- Then you will discover the fullness of your life.
-Brother David Steindl-Rast

Day/Date   Be sure to remember five things to be grateful for every day.

Day/Date   Be sure to remember five things to be grateful for every day.

Day/Date   Be sure to remember five things to be grateful for every day.

Love wholeheartedly, be surprised, give thanks and praise- Then you will discover the fullness of your life.
-Brother David Steindl-Rast

Day/Date   Be sure to remember five things to be grateful for every day.

Day/Date   Be sure to remember five things to be grateful for every day.

Day/Date   Be sure to remember five things to be grateful for every day.

Love wholeheartedly, be surprised, give thanks and praise- Then you will discover the fullness of your life.
-Brother David Steindl-Rast

Day/Date   Be sure to remember five things to be grateful for every day.

Day/Date   Be sure to remember five things to be grateful for every day.

Day/Date   Be sure to remember five things to be grateful for every day.

Love wholeheartedly, be surprised, give thanks and praise- Then you will discover the fullness of your life.
-Brother David Steindl-Rast

Day/Date
Be sure to remember five things to be grateful for every day.

Day/Date
Be sure to remember five things to be grateful for every day.

Day/Date
Be sure to remember five things to be grateful for every day.

Love wholeheartedly, be surprised, give thanks and praise- Then you will discover the fullness of your life.
-Brother David Steindl-Rast

Day/Date   Be sure to remember five things to be grateful for every day.

Day/Date   Be sure to remember five things to be grateful for every day.

Day/Date   Be sure to remember five things to be grateful for every day.

Love wholeheartedly, be surprised, give thanks and praise- Then you will discover the fullness of your life.
-Brother David Steindl-Rast

Day/Date   Be sure to remember five things to be grateful for every day.

Day/Date   Be sure to remember five things to be grateful for every day.

Day/Date   Be sure to remember five things to be grateful for every day.

Love wholeheartedly, be surprised, give thanks and praise- Then you will discover the fullness of your life.
-Brother David Steindl-Rast

Day/Date   Be sure to remember five things to be grateful for every day.

Day/Date   Be sure to remember five things to be grateful for every day.

Day/Date   Be sure to remember five things to be grateful for every day.

Love wholeheartedly, be surprised, give thanks and praise- Then you will discover the fullness of your life.
-Brother David Steindl-Rast

Day/Date   Be sure to remember five things to be grateful for every day.

Day/Date   Be sure to remember five things to be grateful for every day.

Day/Date   Be sure to remember five things to be grateful for every day.

Love wholeheartedly, be surprised, give thanks and praise- Then you will discover the fullness of your life.
-Brother David Steindl-Rast

Day/Date   Be sure to remember five things to be grateful for every day.

Day/Date   Be sure to remember five things to be grateful for every day.

Day/Date   Be sure to remember five things to be grateful for every day.

Love wholeheartedly, be surprised, give thanks and praise- Then you will discover the fullness of your life.
-Brother David Steindl-Rast

Day/Date   Be sure to remember five things to be grateful for every day.

Day/Date   Be sure to remember five things to be grateful for every day.

Day/Date   Be sure to remember five things to be grateful for every day.

Love wholeheartedly, be surprised, give thanks and praise- Then you will discover the fullness of your life.
-Brother David Steindl-Rast

Day/Date   Be sure to remember five things to be grateful for every day.

Day/Date   Be sure to remember five things to be grateful for every day.

Day/Date   Be sure to remember five things to be grateful for every day.

Love wholeheartedly, be surprised, give thanks and praise- Then you will discover the fullness of your life.
-Brother David Steindl-Rast

Day/Date   Be sure to remember five things to be grateful for every day.

Day/Date   Be sure to remember five things to be grateful for every day.

Day/Date   Be sure to remember five things to be grateful for every day.

Love wholeheartedly, be surprised, give thanks and praise- Then you will discover the fullness of your life.
-Brother David Steindl-Rast

Day/Date
Be sure to remember five things to be grateful for every day.

Day/Date
Be sure to remember five things to be grateful for every day.

Day/Date
Be sure to remember five things to be grateful for every day.

Love wholeheartedly, be surprised. give thanks and praise- Then you will discover the fullness of your life.
-Brother David Steindl-Rast

Day/Date   Be sure to remember five things to be grateful for every day.

Day/Date   Be sure to remember five things to be grateful for every day.

Day/Date   Be sure to remember five things to be grateful for every day.

Love wholeheartedly, be surprised, give thanks and praise- Then you will discover the fullness of your life.
-Brother David Steindl-Rast

Day/Date   Be sure to remember five things to be grateful for every day.

Day/Date   Be sure to remember five things to be grateful for every day.

Day/Date   Be sure to remember five things to be grateful for every day.

Love wholeheartedly, be surprised, give thanks and praise- Then you will discover the fullness of your life.
-Brother David Steindl-Rast

Day/Date
Be sure to remember five things to be grateful for every day.

Day/Date
Be sure to remember five things to be grateful for every day.

Day/Date
Be sure to remember five things to be grateful for every day.

Love wholeheartedly, be surprised, give thanks and praise- Then you will discover the fullness of your life.
-Brother David Steindl-Rast

Day/Date   Be sure to remember five things to be grateful for every day.

Day/Date   Be sure to remember five things to be grateful for every day.

Day/Date   Be sure to remember five things to be grateful for every day.

Love wholeheartedly, be surprised, give thanks and praise- Then you will discover the fullness of your life.
-Brother David Steindl-Rast

Day/Date   Be sure to remember five things to be grateful for every day.

Day/Date   Be sure to remember five things to be grateful for every day.

Day/Date   Be sure to remember five things to be grateful for every day.

Love wholeheartedly, be surprised, give thanks and praise- Then you will discover the fullness of your life.
-Brother David Steindl-Rast

Day/Date   Be sure to remember five things to be grateful for every day.

Day/Date   Be sure to remember five things to be grateful for every day.

Day/Date   Be sure to remember five things to be grateful for every day.

Love wholeheartedly, be surprised, give thanks and praise- Then you will discover the fullness of your life.
-Brother David Steindl-Rast

Day/Date   Be sure to remember five things to be grateful for every day.

Day/Date   Be sure to remember five things to be grateful for every day.

Day/Date   Be sure to remember five things to be grateful for every day.

Love wholeheartedly, be surprised, give thanks and praise- Then you will discover the fullness of your life.
-Brother David Steindl-Rast

Day/Date   Be sure to remember five things to be grateful for every day.

Day/Date   Be sure to remember five things to be grateful for every day.

Day/Date   Be sure to remember five things to be grateful for every day.

Love wholeheartedly, be surprised, give thanks and praise- Then you will discover the fullness of your life.
-Brother David Steindl-Rast

Day/Date   Be sure to remember five things to be grateful for every day.

Day/Date   Be sure to remember five things to be grateful for every day.

Day/Date   Be sure to remember five things to be grateful for every day.

Love wholeheartedly, be surprised, give thanks and praise- Then you will discover the fullness of your life.
-Brother David Steindl-Rast

Day/Date   Be sure to remember five things to be grateful for every day.

Day/Date   Be sure to remember five things to be grateful for every day.

Day/Date   Be sure to remember five things to be grateful for every day.

Love wholeheartedly, be surprised, give thanks and praise- Then you will discover the fullness of your life.
-Brother David Steindl-Rast

Day/Date   Be sure to remember five things to be grateful for every day.

Day/Date   Be sure to remember five things to be grateful for every day.

Day/Date   Be sure to remember five things to be grateful for every day.

Love wholeheartedly, be surprised, give thanks and praise- Then you will discover the fullness of your life.
-Brother David Steindl-Rast

Day/Date   Be sure to remember five things to be grateful for every day.

Day/Date   Be sure to remember five things to be grateful for every day.

Day/Date   Be sure to remember five things to be grateful for every day.

Love wholeheartedly, be surprised, give thanks and praise- Then you will discover the fullness of your life.
-Brother David Steindl-Rast

Day/Date   Be sure to remember five things to be grateful for every day.

Day/Date   Be sure to remember five things to be grateful for every day.

Day/Date   Be sure to remember five things to be grateful for every day.

Love wholeheartedly, be surprised, give thanks and praise- Then you will discover the fullness of your life.
-Brother David Steindl-Rast

Day/Date   Be sure to remember five things to be grateful for every day.

Day/Date   Be sure to remember five things to be grateful for every day.

Day/Date   Be sure to remember five things to be grateful for every day.

Love wholeheartedly, be surprised, give thanks and praise- Then you will discover the fullness of your life.
-Brother David Steindl-Rast

Day/Date   Be sure to remember five things to be grateful for every day.

Day/Date   Be sure to remember five things to be grateful for every day.

Day/Date   Be sure to remember five things to be grateful for every day.

Love wholeheartedly, be surprised, give thanks and praise- Then you will discover the fullness of your life.
-Brother David Steindl-Rast

Day/Date   Be sure to remember five things to be grateful for every day.

Day/Date   Be sure to remember five things to be grateful for every day.

Day/Date   Be sure to remember five things to be grateful for every day.

Love wholeheartedly, be surprised, give thanks and praise- Then you will discover the fullness of your life.
-Brother David Steindl-Rast

Day/Date   Be sure to remember five things to be grateful for every day.

Day/Date   Be sure to remember five things to be grateful for every day.

Day/Date   Be sure to remember five things to be grateful for every day.

Love wholeheartedly, be surprised, give thanks and praise- Then you will discover the fullness of your life.
-Brother David Steindl-Rast

Day/Date   Be sure to remember five things to be grateful for every day.

Day/Date   Be sure to remember five things to be grateful for every day.

Day/Date   Be sure to remember five things to be grateful for every day.

Love wholeheartedly, be surprised, give thanks and praise- Then you will discover the fullness of your life.
-Brother David Steindl-Rast

Day/Date   Be sure to remember five things to be grateful for every day.

Day/Date   Be sure to remember five things to be grateful for every day.

Day/Date   Be sure to remember five things to be grateful for every day.

Love wholeheartedly, be surprised, give thanks and praise- Then you will discover the fullness of your life.
-Brother David Steindl-Rast

Day/Date   Be sure to remember five things to be grateful for every day.

Day/Date   Be sure to remember five things to be grateful for every day.

Day/Date   Be sure to remember five things to be grateful for every day.

Love wholeheartedly, be surprised, give thanks and praise- Then you will discover the fullness of your life.
-Brother David Steindl-Rast

Day/Date   Be sure to remember five things to be grateful for every day.

Day/Date   Be sure to remember five things to be grateful for every day.

Day/Date   Be sure to remember five things to be grateful for every day.

Love wholeheartedly, be surprised, give thanks and praise- Then you will discover the fullness of your life.
-Brother David Steindl-Rast

Day/Date   Be sure to remember five things to be grateful for every day.

Day/Date   Be sure to remember five things to be grateful for every day.

Day/Date   Be sure to remember five things to be grateful for every day.

Love wholeheartedly, be surprised, give thanks and praise- Then you will discover the fullness of your life.
-Brother David Steindl-Rast

Day/Date   Be sure to remember five things to be grateful for every day.

Day/Date   Be sure to remember five things to be grateful for every day.

Day/Date   Be sure to remember five things to be grateful for every day.

Love wholeheartedly, be surprised, give thanks and praise- Then you will discover the fullness of your life.
-Brother David Steindl-Rast

Day/Date   Be sure to remember five things to be grateful for every day.

Day/Date   Be sure to remember five things to be grateful for every day.

Day/Date   Be sure to remember five things to be grateful for every day.

Love wholeheartedly, be surprised, give thanks and praise- Then you will discover the fullness of your life.
-Brother David Steindl-Rast

Day/Date   Be sure to remember five things to be grateful for every day.

Day/Date   Be sure to remember five things to be grateful for every day.

Day/Date   Be sure to remember five things to be grateful for every day.

Love wholeheartedly, be surprised, give thanks and praise- Then you will discover the fullness of your life.
-Brother David Steindl-Rast

Day/Date   Be sure to remember five things to be grateful for every day.

Day/Date   Be sure to remember five things to be grateful for every day.

Day/Date   Be sure to remember five things to be grateful for every day.

Love wholeheartedly, be surprised, give thanks and praise- Then you will discover the fullness of your life.
-Brother David Steindl-Rast

Day/Date
Be sure to remember five things to be grateful for every day.

Day/Date
Be sure to remember five things to be grateful for every day.

Day/Date
Be sure to remember five things to be grateful for every day.

Love wholeheartedly, be surprised, give thanks and praise- Then you will discover the fullness of your life.
-Brother David Steindl-Rast

Day/Date   Be sure to remember five things to be grateful for every day.

Day/Date   Be sure to remember five things to be grateful for every day.

Day/Date   Be sure to remember five things to be grateful for every day.

Love wholeheartedly, be surprised, give thanks and praise- Then you will discover the fullness of your life.
-Brother David Steindl-Rast

Day/Date   Be sure to remember five things to be grateful for every day.

Day/Date   Be sure to remember five things to be grateful for every day.

Day/Date   Be sure to remember five things to be grateful for every day.

Love wholeheartedly, be surprised, give thanks and praise- Then you will discover the fullness of your life.
-Brother David Steindl-Rast

Day/Date
Be sure to remember five things to be grateful for every day.

Day/Date
Be sure to remember five things to be grateful for every day.

Day/Date
Be sure to remember five things to be grateful for every day.

Love wholeheartedly, be surprised, give thanks and praise- Then you will discover the fullness of your life.
-Brother David Steindl-Rast

Day/Date   Be sure to remember five things to be grateful for every day.

Day/Date   Be sure to remember five things to be grateful for every day.

Day/Date   Be sure to remember five things to be grateful for every day.

Love wholeheartedly, be surprised, give thanks and praise- Then you will discover the fullness of your life.
-Brother David Steindl-Rast

Day/Date   Be sure to remember five things to be grateful for every day.

Day/Date   Be sure to remember five things to be grateful for every day.

Day/Date   Be sure to remember five things to be grateful for every day.

Love wholeheartedly, be surprised, give thanks and praise- Then you will discover the fullness of your life.
-Brother David Steindl-Rast

Day/Date   Be sure to remember five things to be grateful for every day.

Day/Date   Be sure to remember five things to be grateful for every day.

Day/Date   Be sure to remember five things to be grateful for every day.

Love wholeheartedly, be surprised, give thanks and praise- Then you will discover the fullness of your life.
-Brother David Steindl-Rast

Day/Date   Be sure to remember five things to be grateful for every day.

Day/Date   Be sure to remember five things to be grateful for every day.

Day/Date   Be sure to remember five things to be grateful for every day.

Love wholeheartedly, be surprised, give thanks and praise- Then you will discover the fullness of your life.
-Brother David Steindl-Rast

Day/Date   Be sure to remember five things to be grateful for every day.

Day/Date   Be sure to remember five things to be grateful for every day.

Day/Date   Be sure to remember five things to be grateful for every day.

Love wholeheartedly, be surprised, give thanks and praise- Then you will discover the fullness of your life.
-Brother David Steindl-Rast

Day/Date   Be sure to remember five things to be grateful for every day.

Day/Date   Be sure to remember five things to be grateful for every day.

Day/Date   Be sure to remember five things to be grateful for every day.

Love wholeheartedly, be surprised, give thanks and praise- Then you will discover the fullness of your life.
-Brother David Steindl-Rast

Day/Date   Be sure to remember five things to be grateful for every day.

Day/Date   Be sure to remember five things to be grateful for every day.

Day/Date   Be sure to remember five things to be grateful for every day.